for Annette, in

FLOWERS
IN THE
WINDOW

Life-Enriching Thoughts and Memories of Friends

from Sandra Salt,
the Publisher.

SMH

At Pear Tree Cottage table

INTRODUCTION

Such a simple thing to do: pick flowers in the garden, or buy them in a shop and put them in the window. They'll give you pleasure, sitting there, against the glass – whatever background lies beyond – and pleasure to passers-by.

"Look," some will say, "how lovely – flowers in that window! I should put some in mine."

This is how our little book came about. With posters in the porch and notes in the service sheets, I invited people in St Nicholas' Church, Arundel, including visitors, to let me have short pieces about life-enriching thoughts and memories they would like to share with others.

The result is a collection of pieces, some poetry, some prose some with illustrations, but all – we hope you will find – worthy to be put between the pages of FLOWERS IN THE WINDOW.

Sandra Saer,
Arundel
2016

CONTENTS

1. SOFTLY

Softly, the leaves of memory fall.
Gently, I gather and treasure them all.

Unseen, unheard, you are always near –
so missed, so loved, so very dear.

Soft falls the light from the stars above,
glinting and twinkling their message of love.

Unseen, unheard, you are always near –
so missed, so loved, so very dear.

Silent, the words to my whispered love;
Unseen, unheard, you are always near –
so missed, so loved, so very dear.

and

FRIENDSHIP

When the golden sun is shining
and your heart from care is free
When of others you are thinking,
won't you sometimes think of me?

Think of me when you are lonely.
Plant for me a tender spot

in the warmth of your affection –
plant a sweet forget-me-not.

Shirley Robertson

2. YESTERYEAR

Where are the friends of yesteryear,
with whom along some cloistered walk,
I used to wander and to talk
of human life, and how we should resolve
the old equations, love and lust,
and rich and poor,
and Peace and War?

Roy MacGregor-Hastie

Remembrance flowers by Sue Marsh

3. GRRRRR!

God created Sussex, and then came Boxgrove men –
Then, the Celt and Roman, the Saxon and the Norman,
To add to God's own plan.
First, they farmed the Downland, then the coastal plain,
Then turned the Wealden Forest, into fields of grain.
One cathedral city, pretty market towns,
Castles, churches, villages, all set in God's domain.
Then came the railway, and the ghastly urban sprawl;
Then the smelly motor-car.
Together with the greed o man
Threatens to destroy it all.
I'd sooner live with God's Weald and Downs
Than go to hell with Eco-towns!

Bill Beere

(An explanation from Diana Ayling:

'Written by Mr Beere, when he was very upset with the FORD plans for thousands of houses to be built on farm-land.')

4. THE PATH

If my soul were to speak
What would it say, this day?
Would it tell of sorrow, joy, luck, or pain?
Or higher moments,
or of winter rain?

Would it touch you, like a burning spear,
set your heart alight
and quell your fear,
or settle meekly down
like still waters hide the hungry, waiting weir?

Can it grasp the moment;
shout the hour;
let not a single second
time devour?
Or run the race,
walk the path,
find at last
the golden tower?

O hope, O fate, O all thy steps walk steadfast!
Guide me, O Thou Great Jehovah,
guide my soul, my heart –
never let this servant lose Your path.

Terry Tunmore 15.1.2015

5. WINDOW SPACE*

A smattering of dawn challenges the night sky,
severing earth from heaven,
in long line, growing pale pink and yellow
across my window space.

Then, as if on nature's cue,
a gaggle of gossamer clouds,
cream and unruly edged,
float by,
blown by a soft breeze,
soft as first-love kiss.

I watch all this, wondering
at the unhurried yet inevitable
light, dancing out of darkness.
Now, blinding sunshine
adds dazzle to the day's light...

Clearly reflected in all this drama
is the beginning of a new life
Here, in this waiting place.

* * * * *

I rise, smiling,
To close the curtain on my window space.
At curtain fall, I leave the stage
and glide into the wings.
From there, I fly away
to search for new delights
in my own new day.

Sandra Saer

*the first poem written in Arundel, April, 2010, after I
moved to Caen Stone Court, in February of that year.

6. IN MEMORY OF JUNO

Between 1991 and 2004, a beautiful retriever named Juno began putting paw to pen, writing 'Tails from the Vicarage'. *Those glimpses into life through a dog's eyes began at Arundel Vicarage; later, at Lymington Vicarage. Here is one of his monthly letters.*

I FEEL LIKE A HOLIDAY! \BUT DOES ANYBODY EVER LISTEN TO ME? No, I don't think so. My master and mistress are planning their first trip away, with the caravan, without me! Just because Roddy has returned from University doesn't mean that they can hand over their responsibilities. Last weekend, they (M & M) went to the Island with Ben and Kate, just for an evening meal. Now they know how much I enjoy that boat trip. OK, so it was the evening, and it was raining, but…

I was looking over my mistress's shoulder the other day and saw an interesting article entitled Did Jesus own a dog?' Apparently, a performance-poet called John Hegley, in his poem 'The Easter Story, according to St Bernard', wrote about a dog finding herself trapped in Jesus's tomb, where 'she barked loud enough to waken the dead, which she did'. I shall be interested to take a closer look at the Easter Garden in St Thomas's Church this year, just to see if this is true. It wouldn't surprise me at all if Jesus did have someone like me as a friend, especially after reading the article, that the word DOG is a reflection of GOD.

Well, you are probably thinking that the canine department at the Vicarage has swallowed a dictionary, but my thoughts haven't been entirely taken up with the deeper meaning of life, because it's on my doggy 'List of Things to D' to pop into Karen's Pets and see if they sell Easter eggs. I just don't believe in this malicious rumour that chocolate is bad for dogs!

With love, from Juno

Suzanne Weaver

7. BEECHEN LANE

The Methodist Church stood solid, proud,
its façade set high on steps, looking out
changeless yet full of change.
And here, a moment clasped, to
mark the passing of gentle Joyce.
Her children gathered now,
clothed as men – not young –
with children of their own.
And I? I came to lead my mother
to the passing of her friend;
to stand with her before the box
wherein lay a life – and flowers, adorned.

He stood, white-haired, my childhood friend.
A friend then met and company enjoyed;
his mother gone...
Our childhood spent in laughter and in tear,
with confidences whispered –
but not fully understood.
Without comprehension, I gazed upon
his father, soon to leave, his mother in searing pain,
but now I understand – my adult years have taught.
Then: tea in the garden, walks down Beechen Lane,
grass fights, water fights, and plans for the future
when we were grown.

He stood, my childhood friend,
a man, known only as a boy.
Then, with trousers to his knees,
and socks just short in joining.
And I? brown Clark's upon my feet;
thin-legged, sandalled, scraped, and bony.
Days long and sheltered.
Here, now, my childhood friend – a man not known
To stranger's eyes, a man of age, but my eyes
can only see the b – this man, this boy.

Time has no use for the pendulum,
as it slips buy.

Alison Miller

8. SEND IN THE CLOWNS!

On a cold Saturday evening in November, thirty years ago, Betty and I, dressed as clowns, walked out of our new home, Mews House, to get into our car, when a couple called out, "Have a good party!"

The following morning, we crossed the road, and as we were about to enter St Nicholas' Church, the same couple stopped us, and asked, "Was it a good party?" We answered, "Yes, it was". They invited us to their home for a drink, after church.

And that is how we met Mike and Joyce Michael, who became our best friends in Arundel.

Over the next few weeks, these two lovely people introduced us to more Arundel folk than we had known in Goring-by-Sea, where we had lived previously, for eighteen years.

I cherish many very happy memories of times spent with Mike and Joyce. Mike died in 2002. Joyce continues to be my best pal in Arundel.

Joe Hayes

Joyce and Mike

9. IF I COULD BE AN ELEPHANT

If I could be an Elephant
For only just one day,
I'd use my trunk to water flowers
And help the firemen spray,
I'd blow fresh air to cool them down
And fan them with my ears,
Then tickle them from far awy
Whilst drinking all their beers!

I'd pick up litter with my tusks,
Then stomp off to the dump,
And roar as loudly as I could
To drown out Donald Trump!

But of all things I'd like to do
There's one that is the best –
I'd give the world a Memory
Lest We Forget the rest.

Indigo Ashworth

10. PROUD ACHIEVEMENT

A memory which is blazed indelibly in my heart and mind is the moment I reached the end of the final mile of my Gold Duke of Edinburgh final expedition. After 80 km, several blisters, four nights under a thin sheet of canvas bitterly cold wind, muddy swamps, navigational nightmares, barely suppressed dismay, and seemingly endless walking, I had achieved my goal.

Sitting on a Welsh train platform, feeling the relief of rest through my aching limbs, and the sheer elation from the success of a mountainous feat, I've never been so proud.

Amelia Saer

A North Wales landscape

11. A MOTHER'S SAYING

'Patience and perseverance made a bishop of His Reverence!'

(W. M-H)

12. HOW WONDERFUL TO BE ME!

How wonderful to be myself,
Peering upon every shelf,
As I explore the world with glee
I think –
How wonderful it is to be me!

Anna Heseltine

13. ON LOVE

What it is to love!
We have all loved something,
somewhere – someone.

Love is annihilating in its intensity;
devastating in its tenderness;
uplifting to our heart's delight.

Never mind the night.
Never mind the day.
Love is always there.
Everywhere.
Every way.

Sandra Saer

14. THE TORN CURTAIN

The night is coming. Do you feel the darkness, black smoke curling under doors, doors that are locked? The time has come to consider the touch of heaven on earth. Stand up to find some light, a scent of Daffodils. Where does this come from? There, down among the rubble, I see a little flower pushing itself up, to catch a last ray of sunlight. These flowers, few though they may be, teach us, urge us to persevere. Lift up your eyes! Hold on to others.

The Day is coming. Focus on the Day. See! the curtain has been torn from top to bottom. Go through the torn curtain with me.

Emilie Bruell

Notes from Emilie:

'And the veil of the temple was rent in twain from the top to bottom.' (Mark, 15:38)

'It bespeaks a great deal of comfort to all believing Christians, for it signifies the consecrating and laying open to us of a new and living way into the holiest by the blood of Jesus.' (from Matthew Henry's *Commentary*)

'And He will destroy in this mountain the face of the covering cast over all people, and the vail that is spread over all nations.' (Isaiah 25:7)

15. OZYMANDIAS

by Percy Bysshe Shelley*

I met a traveller from an antique land
Who said: "Two vast and trunkless legs of stone
Stand in the desert. Near them, on the sand,
Half sunk, a shattered visage lies, whose frown,
And wrinkled lip, and sneer of cold command,
Tell that its sculptor well those passions read
Which yet survive, stamped on these lifeless things,
The hand that mocked them and the heart that fed:
And on the pedestal these words appear:
'My name is Ozyandias, king of kings:
Look on my works, ye Mighty, and despair!'
Nothing beside remains. Round the decay
Of that colossal wreck, boundless and bare
The lone and level sands stretch far away."

(Contributed by **Daniel Hodson,** as
'An unique exercise in proper humility')

Flowers in The Window

16. REFLECTIONS OF A ONE-EYED MUGWUMP

I am a Mugwump siting on a fence,
Face one side and wump on the other.
I don't blame the innocents –
But I do blame my mother!

Mugwumps were bold, Mugwumps brave.
Mother said "Learn to heed the other view".
In argument, discussion and opinionated rave,
Now it's axiomatic, we prevaricate, don't you?

O maligned, cyclopic*, misunderstood percher,
Noble intention, to prize another's notion.
It is the product of such enlightened nurture,
Hold my hand and cradle my emotion.

David Farrer

David was one of the seven winners in a 2012 Poetry Competition, when readers of the *Chichester Observer* and *Worthing Herald* were invited to send in poems along the lines of those in Patrick Moore's *Within The Glade – Poems for Children* – of all ages!, about a bird or animal (including Mugwumps!) given human characteristics.

'As a small child, I managed to lose one of Mugwump's eyes. Somehow a one-eyed Mugwump seems incongruous...

'I had a toy Mugwump rather than a bear. I knew his innermost thoughts long before I knew of Mark Twain and his fellow political Mugwumps'.

More recently, David described a Mugwump as 'a very benign creature, who sits on the fence in a pathetic attempt to please everyone, and is at once a creature of great comfort and the butt of the certainty freaks of this life.'

17. HOW WE CAME TO DELL QUAY

I rode here on the back of a turtle, sitting cross-legged, half-lotus, facing the way we had come, looking back towards the wake. We left no wake, we moved with the swell, we seemed to drift, but the turtle as using his arm, his strongly ungainly flippers, and his mouth as fixed in an ancient grimace of forbearance. We followed the ocean currents, the global vortices that coaxed the trades along; and we sought the empty places through the trackless ways, over the dip of the world, forever falling and turning. We met ships and whales freighting craft low in the water, wounding and churning the water to frenzy, and we let ourselves be dragged along in the mile-wide wake of milk and emerald, then midnight blue, as we ducked and dived beneath the world and kicked our heels at the sun and pressed our faces through the chill, then downwards to the stars and moons which breathed cold silver into our eyes and melted the scales of the patient turtle, who sparkled hard as amber in the night.

In time, we came upon this place and saw it suited us. The men had not yet come. Perhaps they will, never will. Perhaps this is a story not yet written, yes, but buried in the sand.

I must warn the turtle of this, lest he scratch these stories from the sand.

James Rodgers

18. THE SONG BIRD

A spirit of unknown finesse
Awakes the watchful towers,
Resuffles time in honest phase
And soothes the cosmic showers.

Your peace can calm the deep distress
That haunts the midnight hours,
A light that keep the dark at bay
And softly scents the flowers.

To sing this song, of love so strong
For one that few will know,
You fly alone the greet the day
And walk where none may go.

Caspian Ashworth

Flowers in The Window

19. THE BOY IN THE RIVER

Cool, gentle stream, breathing its sigh of ripples
On its ever-changing brow,
Never stops to pause or wonder how.

It's so clear, powdered with the blue of a sunny day.
It's not so deep, and yet if one should wonder at its depth,
disturb it's ultra calm
and interrupt the play of weeds upon its bed,
one could easily find one's dead.

Dave Pidoux

(Dave writes: *The New River* was created in 1613 to supply
drinking water to London. It ran for twenty miles, from Hertford to
Clissold Park, Stoke Newington. When a schoolboy tragically
drowned in the river around the mid-1950s, the authorities decided
to lay a large, underground water pipe, for the New River to flow
through, so that section of the river disappeared for ever. To this
day, that sad site at Clissold Park remains covered in grass.')

20. CHRISTMAS GREENERY FOR ST. NICHOLAS

It all began nearly thirty years ago. What fun, I thought, if we wound greenery around the church's pillars; "decked", as Joe Hayes's daughter later said, "the hall with holly"! We set strings down the aisles and laid the longest strands of ivy we could find along these. Shooing the youngest of our children off our burgeoning strings, we tied the greenery on, and decorated the whole with red ribbons. Then the fun really started!

My husband and Father Michael Weaver bravely took the very longest ladders and climbed up, to tie our garlands round the capitals, while we clambered round and round the pews, so that the garlands encircled the pillars. It was so enjoyable and in those early, less perfectionist days, nobody seemed to mind that one of our garlands was wound the opposite way to the other five! (Not that I could have persuaded John and Fr. Michael to climb those slippy ladder, again, even if they had!)

These days, we are rather more 'professional' in our decorations and, while my dear colleagues create superb flower arrangements, I seem somehow unable to escape from my love of garlands.

Into the woods I tramp, sometimes with a grandchild (who seems capable of carrying no more than two or three branches) and always with the dog. As the light turns yellow and the mud ever deeper, I cut greenery and – the dog wondering why I can't continue to throw her ball – fall down the hill, my arms full of dripping branches.

The ribbons now are velvet with golden edges, not the plasticised red of before, and if you look at the box graves in the churchyard, you will see patterns of holly and yew and ivy: we all spray our branches with gold and these are the outlines left behind, as yet another Christmas delights us all.

Sue Marsh

21. DIVINITY SHED

42 degrees and thinking of the donkeyed mother
Riding for two
Joseph, invisible to history, walking lover.
What to do?
No bookings made, roads packed to honour Roman whim.
The Hilton, Alberge Hilton, doss house house,
chock-filled, brim!

Shed door stands ajar
Quick carpentry fixing broken manger,
Shed of all numen,
Christ is born, brightest star
Of all that's human.
Donkey knows next fare's a'far.

David Farrer

Painting by Charis Saer

22. A COPTIC CHRISTMAS

The artist captures brightly coloured angelic throng
But sheep if sheep they be, are city-wrong.
The cattle, for the most part, have a bovine air
Save one amused goat/deer in front there.
The shepherds keep their garments colourful and clean
While stylish Mary looks in charge, and Joseph – green.
The babe, alas, the one we come to see,
Is older and too well-haired in such a crib to be.
For all of that, there is a certain spark
Proper for one who lightens the dark.

David Farrer

23. WINTER COMES...

Winter comes, slowly,
yet unexpectedly
(not always welcome)
out of autumn.
Rogue frosts sneak down, searing
the last of the beans
hanging on for picking, in the garden.

The old find the cold difficult to bear,
retreating inside to
reassuring warmth, and bed.

Winter comes quickly, cruelly,
to the aching heart.
Cold replaces the heat
of love known, then lost.

Yet winter has winning ways –
cosy evenings in this cottage;
a log fire lit and warming.
The Rayburn, too,
Now has its *moment de gloire:*
heating, cooking; bringing back to life
frozen fingers, just in
from bean-pod foraging.

And the real plus?
The coming of Christmas.

Winter comes.
Soon, though,
my mother's first snowdrops
will certainly appear
(they do so every year.)
And spring will come.
It's just a God-step away.

Sandra Saer